MY SIXTH
2 in 1 COLLECTION
CONTAINS:

THE MUSIC LOVER
THE MASTER CHEF

SNOOPY

(features as)

The Music Lover

Charles M. Schulz

10-16

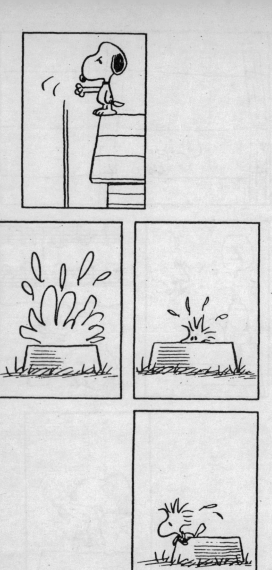

TELEPHONE

IF THE COUNTESS HADN'T TURNED HIM DOWN, WOULD YOU BUY ME SOMETHING?

4-6

10-26

5-14

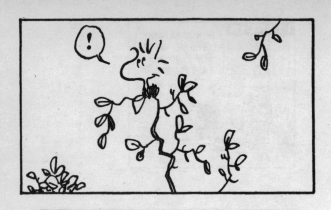

© 1977 United Feature Syndicate, Inc.

7-31

4-28

© 1977 United Feature Syndicate, Inc.

4-26

9-10

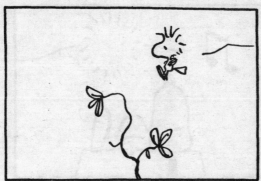

8-6

8-20

© 1980 United Feature Syndicate, Inc.

2-18

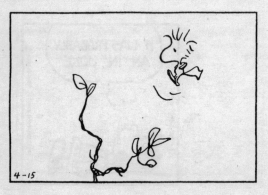

4-15

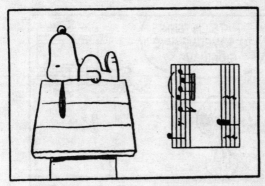

© 1979 United Feature Syndicate, Inc.

12-27

4-17

11-10

BOING!!

© 1984 United Feature Syndicate, Inc.

9-18

© 1983 United Feature Syndicate, Inc.

KLUNK!!

TIME OUT FOR REGROUPING, MA'AM

I BROUGHT SOME OF MY VACATION PICTURES FOR YOU TO SEE, SCHROEDER, BUT I GUESS YOU'RE BUSY...

WHY DON'T I JUST LEAVE THEM HERE, AND YOU CAN LOOK AT THEM LATER?

4-30

© 1987 United Feature Syndicate, Inc.

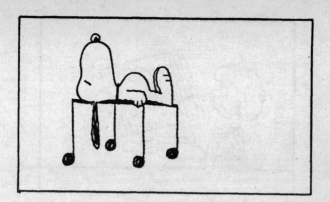

9-14

10-10 © 1989 United Feature Syndicate, Inc.

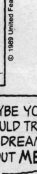

© 1988 United Feature Syndicate, Inc

SNOOPY

(features as)

The Master Chef

Charles M. Schulz

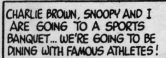

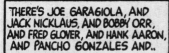

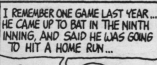

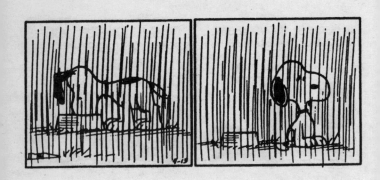

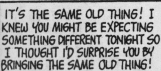

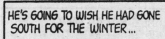

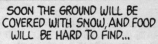

1-4

CHOMP
CHOMP
CHOMP

WOODSTOCK IS THE ONLY PERSON
I KNOW WHO CAN BLOW HIS
MIND ON BREAD CRUMBS...

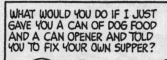

WHAT WOULD YOU DO IF I JUST GAVE YOU A CAN OF DOG FOOD AND A CAN OPENER AND TOLD YOU TO FIX YOUR OWN SUPPER?

WAAH!

WHAT DID HE THINK I'D DO, JOIN A WOLF PACK?

3-25

WOODSTOCK FEELS THAT
EATING BREAD CRUMBS IS
KIND OF DEGRADING...

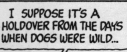

6-9

© 1977 United Feature Syndicate, Inc.

WELL, GO AHEAD, AND EAT.. WHAT ARE YOU WAITING FOR?

I WAS HOPING THERE WAS A SALAD BAR

MAJOR FUNDING FOR
THIS MEAL WAS
PROVIDED BY A GRANT
FROM OUR FAMILY

12-28

IF THEY HAVE A
PLEDGE NIGHT,
I'M LEAVING!

THERE'S ONLY ONE PROBLEM WITH EATING IN THE RAIN...

© 1981 United Feature Syndicate, Inc.

IT TENDS TO COOL DOWN YOUR PIZZA

DON'T YOU EVER DO ANYTHING TO MAKE HIS DINNER LOOK NICE?

9-12

I HOPE YOU APPRECIATE MY FIXING YOUR SUPPER FOR YOU EVERY NIGHT...

NATURALLY..

HERE... HAVE A BITE!

DOG FOOD! I'VE NEVER UNDERSTOOD HOW YOU CAN EAT THAT STUFF...

IT'S AN ACQUIRED TASTE

© 1983 United Feature Syndicate, Inc.   7-28

DID YOU SEE THAT? I BROUGHT YOUR SUPPER OUT ON ONE FINGER!

8-25

© 1984 United Feature Syndicate, Inc.

AND I ATE THE WHOLE THING WITH ONE STOMACH!

SUPPERTIME ISN'T FOR ANOTHER HOUR...

AND STOP STARING AT THE BACK DOOR..IT MAKES ME NERVOUS!

THAT'S THE IDEA

Other PEANUTS titles published by Ravette . . .

Gift Books (hardcover)		**ISBN**	**Price**
A Friend is ... forever	(new)	1 84161 213 8	£4.99
Happiness is ... a warm puppy	(new)	1 84161 211 1	£4.99
Love is ... walking hand in hand	(new)	1 84161 212 X	£4.99
Security is ... a thumb and a blanket	(new)	1 84161 210 3	£4.99

Miscellaneous		
Why, Charlie Brown, Why? (hardcover-new)	1 84161 231 6	£6.99
Peanuts Treasury	1 84161 043 7	£9.99
You Really Don't Look 50 Charlie Brown	1 84161 020 8	£7.99

Snoopy's Laughter and Learning		
Book 1 – Read with Snoopy	1 84161 016 X	£2.50
Book 2 – Write with Snoopy	1 84161 017 8	£2.50
Book 3 – Count with Snoopy	1 84161 018 6	£2.50
Book 4 – Colour with Snoopy	1 84161 019 4	£2.50

All PEANUTS books are available at your local bookshop or from the publisher at the address below. Just tick the titles required and send the form with your payment to:-

RAVETTE PUBLISHING
Unit 3, Tristar Centre, Star Road, Partridge Green, West Sussex RH13 8RA

Prices and availability are subject to change without notice.

Please enclose a cheque or postal order made payable to **Ravette Publishing** to the value of the cover price of the book and allow the following for UK postage and packing:

60p for the first book + 30p for each additional book, except ...
You Really Don't Look 50 Charlie Brown – please add £1.50 p&p per copy,
Peanuts Treasury – please add £3.00 p&p per copy,
Colour Collections – please add £2.50 p&p per copy.

Name ....

Address ....

....

....

....